BRAIN CAMP

First Second

New York & London

Text Copyright © 2010 by Susan Kim and Laurence Klavan
Illustrations Copyright © 2010 by Faith Erin Hicks

Published by First Second
First Second is an imprint of Roaring Brook Press,
a division of Holtzbrinck Publishing Holdings Limited Partnership,
175 Fifth Avenue, New York, NY 10010

Distributed in Canada by H. B. Fenn and Company Ltd.
distributed in the United Kingdom by Macmillan Children's Books,
a division of Pan Macmillan.

Design by Colleen AF Venable

Colored by Hilary Sycamore and Sky Blue Ink

Cataloging-in-Publication Data is on file at the Library of Congress.

ISBN: 978-1-59643-704-3

First Second books are available for special promotions and premiums.
For details, contact: Director of Special Markets, Holtzbrinck Publishers.

First Edition August 2010
Printed in June 2010 in China by
South China Printing Co. Ltd., Dongguan City, Guangdong Province
1 3 5 7 9 10 8 6 4 2

BRAIN CAMP

WRITTEN BY SUSAN KIM & LAURENCE KLAVAN
ARTWORK BY FAITH ERIN HICKS
COLOR BY HILARY SYCAMORE

:01
First Second
NEW YORK & LONDON

Meanwhile, across America...

Faster!

Focus!

Higher!

Swing low to high!

In the suburbs of New Jersey...

4

In Queens, New York...

Mrs. Meyer, I'm Mr. Oswald.

I'm from Camp Fielding, America's best new educational summer camp, guaranteed to prepare any child for the SATs and beyond.

Sorry for the late hour.

Well, yes, it is after ten...

We've had two campers withdraw unexpectedly. Based on profiles submitted by schools, we've chosen Lucas for one of these open slots.

I need some coffee.

13

What the—

SLAM!

I'm Dwayne. Welcome to a world without puberty.

I'm Lucas.

Are you replacing Clerkson? That was fast.

What happened... he couldn't hack the work?

Are you kidding? He was the smartest kid in Cabin 3. That's the cabin where the genius boys are—

—which is strange, because last week, I swear they were all exactly like him.

Meanwhile, at the girls' cabin...

GIRLS' CABIN
BOYS' CABIN
POOL

23

24

27

29

—and I'm "hyper" and "clueless."

Okay, people... listen up!

You get five minutes to finish up. Then it's time for the afternoon's activities!

Trust me... she doesn't mean volleyball.

The weird thing is, they don't teach at Camp Fielding. All they do is throw you into a subject and figure you'll just pick it up.

$(\sqrt{7})^2 = r^2 + r^2 - 2^{rr} \cos\left(\frac{2\pi}{3}\right)$

Which is a really weird way to teach someone.

Kunt u wat ik begrijpen zeg?

See what I mean?

32

35

Oww!

Ohhhh no...

44

Only you're coming with us.

No way. I'm not having you drag me through the woods... it's hard enough getting around on asphalt.

Well, we'll go slow then.

Yeah. No problem!

Look, it's not just that... you don't know my parents. This is like the millionth camp I've been to. If I screw up here, they said they're gonna ship me off to some boarding school in Switzerland...

Don't worry, we won't get caught... we promise.

There are windows out back. Let's see if they're open.

Did you see anything? Like a soda machine?

I couldn't see much. Could you?

No.

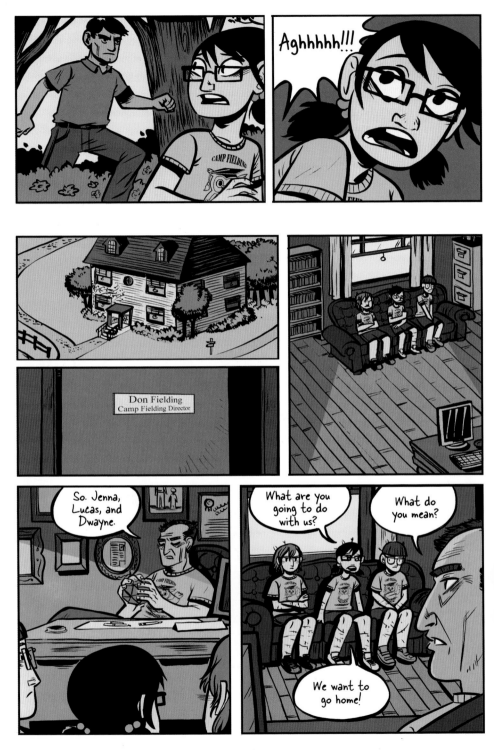

57

My mom calls this a "ten-finger discount."

Why *didn't* he call our parents? You think he's scared we might tell them what we saw?

Like my Mom would ever take my side against any adult.

Yeah. Knowing my folks, I'd probably end up grounded.

But we don't even know what we saw. A bunch of kids yorking up feathers. Maybe it was nothing.

Yeah, right. It happens every day...

Hey... I just thought of something.

A zillion years ago, there was this girl and her mom staying at this hotel. One day, the girl decides to go out shopping...

What? What girl?

It's a story.

So the girl goes shopping and comes back, only her mom's gone. Like vanished.

So the girl complains, and the hotel people go, like, what are you talking about?

And she goes like what happened to my mom? And they go, you don't have a mom...

...you came here by yourself. And she goes oh yeah? And they go yeah. And then she goes—

Back up. What are you getting at?

Shut up, I'm almost finished.

And they go, okay, so what room did you stay in? And she goes, room 414. And they go, we don't even have a room 414. And she goes oh, yeah?

Only when she goes up to the fourth floor...

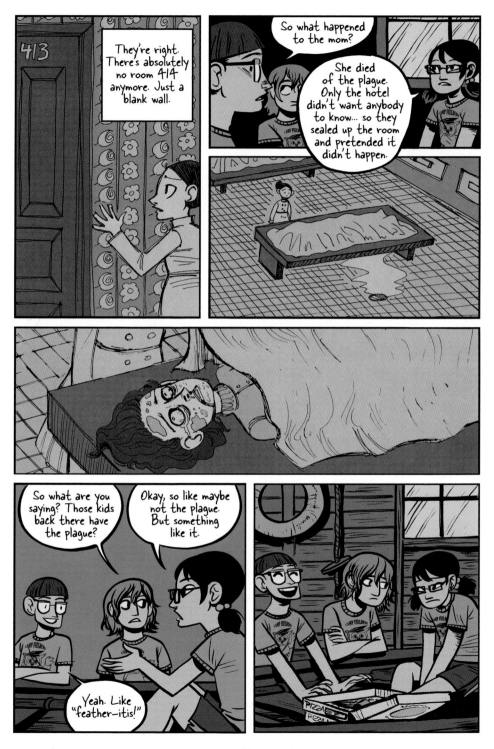

And Fielding and those guys can't risk anybody finding out about it. Or else this whole place would be ruined.

That's crazy...

So just because some thing's crazy it can't be true...

The first thing we should do is get those three kids out.

Just us? How?

Yeah... Fielding's going to be watching us like a hawk.

I can jimmy a window... that's easy. We can do it tomorrow, when nobody's looking. We just have to convince people to help us...

But who's going to believe us?

I don't know. But what choice do we have?

Okay. If you guys take your cabin, I'll do mine!

So how can you seal up a door and paint it while someone's out shopping?

Wouldn't it still be wet?

It's a story. Besides—just because something's crazy doesn't mean it can't be true.

Hi, Jenna.

It's my bunk. I think everyone's infected... look.

Care to join us?

So we'll just do it with the guys, that's all.

Don't worry. It's gonna be okay.

Dwayne's late. We better save him some pizza or he'll be mad.

We should head back, before anyone notices.

What the—

Hey Dwayne?
You okay?

84

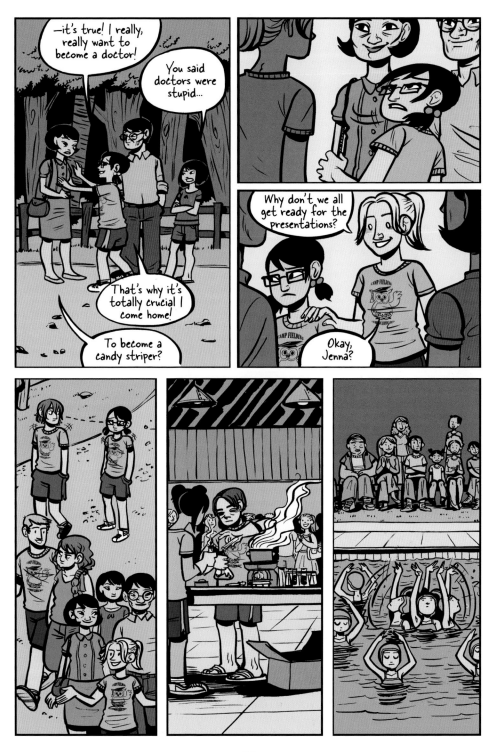

...Is that Sherry and the others?

I'm afraid so. They didn't receive the innoculation.

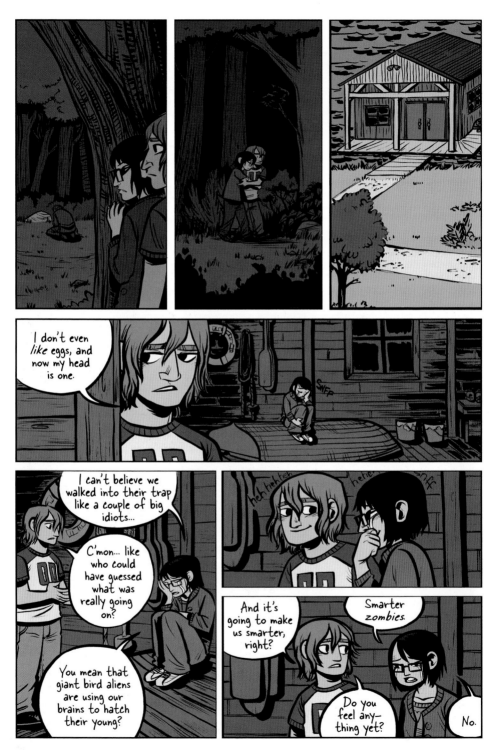

I don't even *like* eggs, and now my head is one.

I can't believe we walked into their trap like a couple of big idiots...

C'mon... like who could have guessed what was really going on?

You mean that giant bird aliens are using our brains to hatch their young?

And it's going to make us smarter, right?

Smarter zombies.

Do you feel any- thing yet?

No.

109

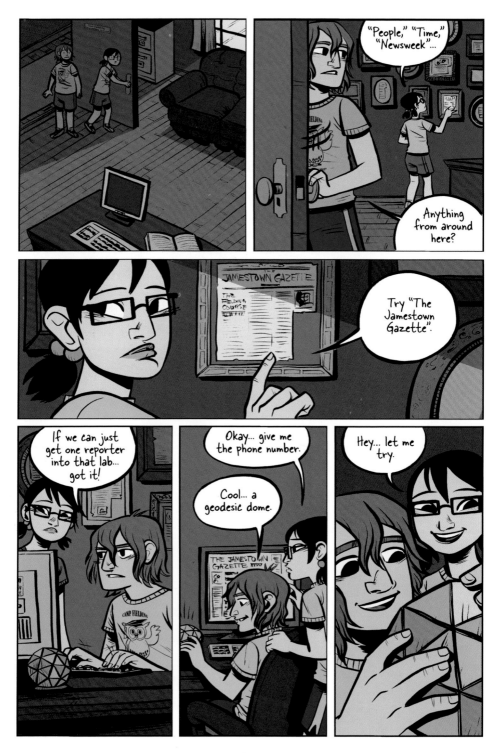

footer: 125

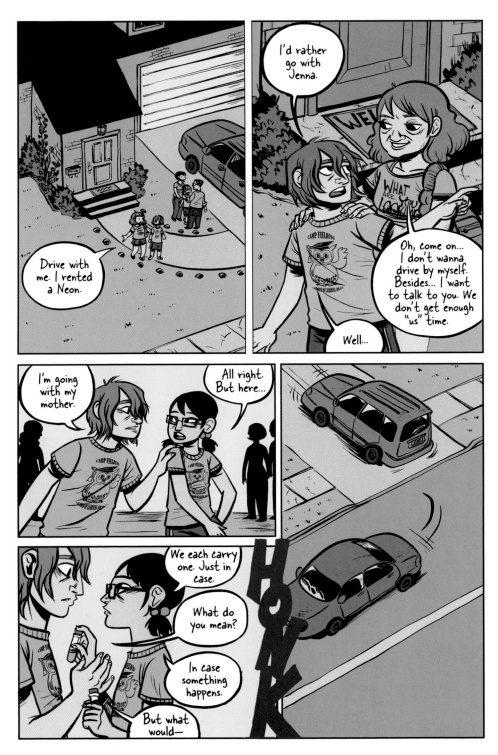

How you doing back there, honey?

Fine.

That's them.

Let's go.

SCREECH

128

Do you still have your half of the solution?
I believe so. But even after we combine them, how can we treat the greatest number of campers before being detected?
That's it. Total immersion... epidermal transmission.
CAMP FIELDING
T-days at two... and it's Thursday.

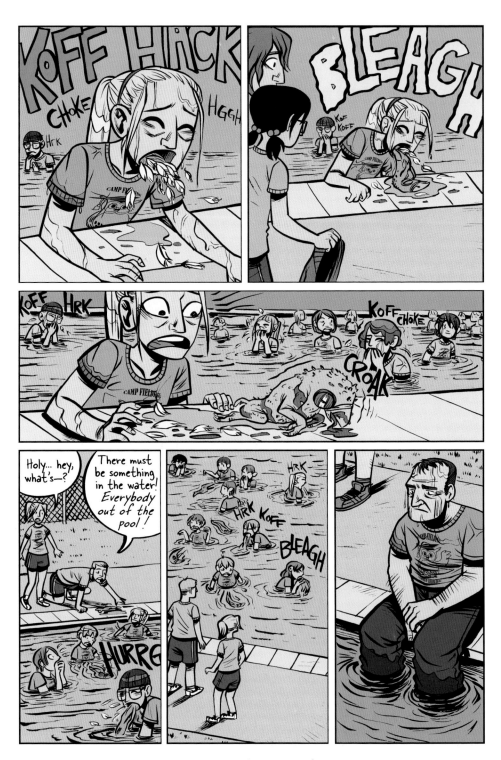

144

Next summer.

Jenna—
My folks are sending
me to a new place,
Camp Ritalin, in the
Poconos. Let me know
what you losers are
up to.
—Dwayne